Getting Started In Magnetic Healing

BURYL PAYNE, PH.D.

COPYRIGHT 1998
ISBN NO. 0-9628569-9-1

PSYCHOPHYSICS PRESS
1803 Mission St., Suite 24
Santa Cruz, CA 95073
(408) 462-1588
www.buryl.com

To John Maz etier for making the clear illustrations of how things move and turn, to Frank Hill, who drew the delightful cartoons to help one see the lighter side of magnetism, and to LeAnn Meyer for her determination to see that words were properly chosen and placed in their proper order and form; and to Antara who created the beautiful cover for this book and arranged all the words, drawings and illustrations with her artistic eye.

TABLE OF CONTENTS

WHY USE MAGNETS?

Magnets provide wonderful first aid for tooth-aches, headaches, backaches, stomach upsets, strains, and most of the odd aches and pains that mysteriously appear now and then in our wonderfully healthy and complex bodies. Magnets can help broken bones heal twice as fast and their use can hasten wound healing and reduce the formation of scar tissue. Magnets can also help the body heal chronic ailments such as arthritis, chronic fatigue syndrome, multiple sclerosis, or Parkinson's disease.

Sounds too good to be true? Try it. Magnets rarely cause side effects and if any do occur they end as soon as the magnet is removed. As with most treatments, the earlier a condition is treated, the faster it will heal.

Magnets are not a cure-all, but they are usually worth trying for any condition, because they work compatibly with any other treatment, including surgery. Join the millions of people who have benefited from magnetic therapy; you won't regret it!

HOW TO USE MAGNETS

THREE BASIC STEPS

1. Place a magnet on any area of injury, pain, or illness.

   Be quiet & relax.

   Focus on your body's response.

   Notice how it feels – better, worse, or no difference.

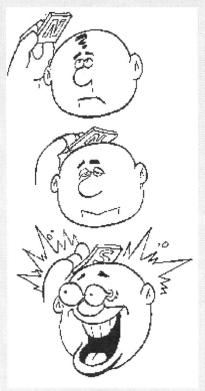

2. If it feels *worse*, turn the magnet over.

3. If it feels *better*, continue using it.

4) If there is no noticeable difference, leave the magnet in place for ten to fifteen minutes. Repeat, with the magnet in the same place facing the same way, 2 or 3 times a day for a few days.

5) If there is no improvement by that time, turn the magnet over and continue its application for a few more days.

6) If you don't notice any improvement within 10 days, then magnets probably won't help. *They won't hurt either.*

If any irritation or pain increases when you apply a magnet, it will usually go away if you turn the magnets over for a few minutes or discontinue using them. However all magnetic therapists agree that tumors,

♥ ♥ ♥ ♥ ♥ ♥

MAGNETIC THERAPY IS *NOT* DANGEROUS

♥ ♥ ♥ ♥ ♥ ♥

cysts, or abnormal cell growths should be only treated with the north polarity. (See Chapter 3 to learn about south and north polarity.)

You have just read the basic principles of magnetic therapy. You don't need to read any more to begin using magnets.

THE IMPORTANCE OF MAGNETISM FOR LIFE

We live in an invisible atmosphere of magnetism more pervasive than the air. This invisible force is present everywhere, from depths below the deepest mine to heights far beyond the highest flying satellite. Called the geomagnetic field, it constantly ebbs and flows like tides. Waves, ripples, and cross currents affect human behavior at every level from the bad to the good, from the trivial to the sublime, from the tiniest electron inside our bodies to the outward color of our hair. Magnetism forms the cradle and context of our lives. Most people have no idea how much their lives are subtly influenced by this all-permeating, ever-changing, invisible force.

If this invisible atmosphere were to disappear, we would fry from the solar particle radiations that are constantly deflected by it. Even if shielded by living underground, our health would quickly deteriorate and our lives would probably shorten. Mice in a laboratory, shielded from natural magnetism, die sooner than controls. Presently the geomagnetic field is declining about 5 percent per century. Nothing to worry about; it has its gradual ups and downs, however, of more immediate importance, the magnetic force of earth does diminish as much as 50 percent inside steel reinforced buildings, boats, or cars. A certain amount of magnetism may be as necessary to our health as vitamins or minerals.

Magnetic material has been found in the human brain, in the brains of dolphins, salmon, pigeons, and other animals. Dr. Frank Brown, a well-known marine biologist, believed that every cell of all living organisms responds to changes in earth's magnetic field. People are very sensitive to such changes, sometimes even too sensitive. Too much change too fast can push some people 'over the edge'.

Dr. Robert Becker, author of *The Body Electric*, and his associates, found that there were more psychiatric admissions at times of rapid changes (called magnetic storms). Other researchers have found that accidents, crimes, lovers quarrels, and wife poisonings, all increased at times of increased solar magnetic activity. If the moon is new or full, things are often worse. (See my other books and articles for more data and references.)

In the most extreme cases, some changes in geomagnetic activity seem to draw human beings irresistibly into international battles every eleven years or so. The bar diagram on the next page shows sunspot peaks and international battles for the 200 years that sunspot records have been kept. Only some of the battles are mentioned.

SOME PEOPLE
BECOME UPSET
WHEN EARTH'S
MAGNETIC FIELD
CHANGES
TOO RAPIDLY.

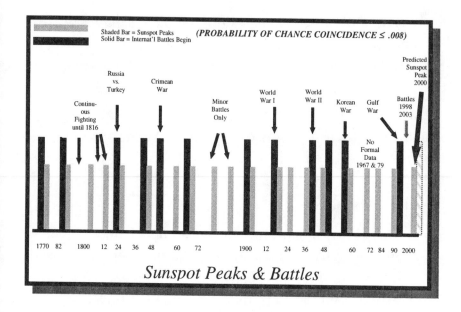

Shaded Bar = Sunspot Peaks
Solid Bar = Internat'l Battles Begin

(PROBABILITY OF CHANCE COINCIDENCE ≤ .008)

Predicted Sunspot Peak 2000

Russia vs. Turkey

Crimean War

Continuous Fighting until 1816

Minor Battles Only

World War I

World War II

Korean War

Gulf War

Battles 1998 2003

No Formal Data 1967 & 79

1770 82   1800   12 24 36 48   60   72   1900 12   24 36 48   60   72 84 90 2000

Sunspot Peaks & Battles

This diagram was prepared from the data of former Professor Raymond Wheeler of the University of Kansas. With the aid of 200 graduate students he ranked every battle on a scale of 1 to 3 for 2,500 years back in time. Contrary to common beliefs that wars are always going on, he found that battles waxed and waned in nearly regular cycles of approximately 11 years. Sunspots have a cycle of about 11 years too, though accurate records are only available for the past 200 years. The diagram above was constructed by plotting the times of *onset* of battles and the maximum of sunspots. *Note that battles never began exactly at the times of peak sunspot activity.* The next outbreak of war should be coming up either a year or two before the predicted sunspot peak in 2000 or just after it, perhaps around 2003. Why before or after and not right on the peaks? Magnetic activity increases the most either just before or just after sunspot peaks, according to Dr. Hundhausen, a Denver geophysicist.

The odds against battles consistently occurring within two years of sunspot peaks are more than ten thousand to one! Yet they did, which suggests that solar/geomagnetic activity is a larger factor in triggering warring behavior than social, political, economic, or ethnic factors.

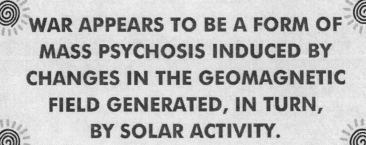

WAR APPEARS TO BE A FORM OF MASS PSYCHOSIS INDUCED BY CHANGES IN THE GEOMAGNETIC FIELD GENERATED, IN TURN, BY SOLAR ACTIVITY.

When the sun's activity changes, more particles from the sun stream to earth and jiggle it's protective magnetic field. When this increases about every 11 years or so, humans, mostly men, become far more aggressive.

Just as PMS overwhelms some women every month, related to the Moon's cycles, MMS (*Male Macho Syndrome*) drives some men to warring behavior every 11 years, in phase with solar cycles. The common mechanism may be magnetic changes, or something presently unknown, that is associated with magnetic changes. It's well known that the Moon plays a part in these lunatic behaviors too, especially when it is new or full and in line with the stream of particles radiating from the Sun.

Eventually, knowledge of this mechanism may help find more effective solutions for the 'disease' of warring behavior.

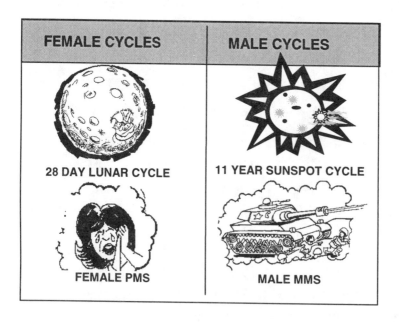

FEMALE CYCLES	MALE CYCLES
28 DAY LUNAR CYCLE	11 YEAR SUNSPOT CYCLE
FEMALE PMS	MALE MMS

Fortunately for us, not all magnetic changes are irritating, or incite all of us to violence. Some types of magnetic activity stimulate humans to greater creativity. Dr. Theodor Landscheidt cites evidence indicating that scientific discoveries, artistic creations, or mystic visions are often triggered when solar flares jostle the geomagnetic field and, hence, our brain waves and biochemistry *(Sun, Earth, and Man*, p. 35 ff). According to G. Gurdjieff, by the use of our will we have the potential to use this extra flux from the Sun either for creative endeavors or for destructive activity.[*]

On the positive side, there are at least two times each year when the weather is extraordinarily balmy and people feel wonderful. These special times occur when Jupiter, Earth, and Sun are in a line. Earth's magnetic field is much calmer at these times. The next alignment will occur on Sept.16 1998, and reoccur February 1, 1999. Expect Indian summers for the next two years.

In contrast, the weather is unseasonably cold and stormy when Earth, Sun, and Pluto align twice a year at regular intervals, moving ahead about two days each year (Pluto travels slowly). This alignment occurs on late May 27, 1998 and November 30, 1998. Once more magnetism seems to be the link.

And so it goes for humans, up and down several times a day, as the geomagnetic field flows in waves and ripples through our bodies. Planets pass each other and move on. Sunspots arise and fade away. Solar radiation's change, and Earth's magnetic field responds by producing tiny wiggles of mag-flux which can alter

---

[*] Predictions of solar and geomagnetic disturbances can now be made. Knowledge helps one to know when to make efforts for constructive activity rather than destructive activity. A software program for the PC is available which shows planetary position in graphic dynamic form. An accompanying text explains the connections between sunspots, geomagnetic activity, and planetary positions. See Ch. 10

brain rhythms, influence hormone production, stimulate plant growth, and can even affect some industrial chemical processes. *We can't escape, but we can slightly alter our own responses if we know even a little about the science of magnetism.*

Natural magnets, formed by Earth's powerful magnetizing or organizing force, have been used for thousands of years to help bodies heal. The first person to discover that a special kind of rock had a healing effect on a body must have been amazed. People are just as amazed today when a simple magnet can take away pain when placed on a sore tooth, knee, or a headache. Although sensitive instruments and experiments have led to new notions about magnetism, the fundamental mystery remains. The next chapter describes some current thinking about the nature of magnetism. Even so, there's no mystery in using magnets to improve health, as you'll see in succeeding chapters.

CHAPTER 2

WHAT ARE MAGNETS?

Atoms link together to form molecules which in turn cluster and clump to form the various substances we know as matter. About 100 years ago atoms, in turn, were discovered to be mostly empty space with clusters of particles called protons and neutrons making up a central nucleus, which much smaller particles whirl around called electrons. Electrons circle the nucleus so fast (over one trillion times a second!) that they look like solid shells to our gross measuring instruments.

The illustration shows these structural levels for iron, the workhorse metal of our society, and the basic

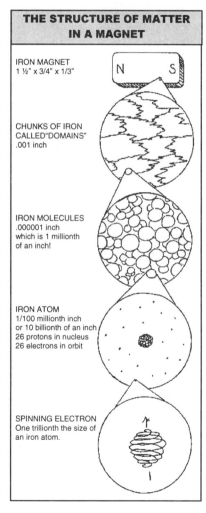

THE STRUCTURE OF MATTER IN A MAGNET

IRON MAGNET
1 ½" x 3/4" x 1/3"

N   S

CHUNKS OF IRON CALLED"DOMAINS"
.001 inch

IRON MOLECULES
.000001 inch
which is 1 millionth of an inch!

IRON ATOM
1/100 millionth inch or 10 billionth of an inch
26 protons in nucleus
26 electrons in orbit

SPINNING ELECTRON
One trillionth the size of an iron atom.

element for magnetic technology.

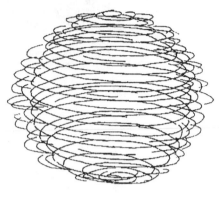

A FUZZY SPINNING ELECTRON CLOUD

Electrons, and the protons and neutrons that form the center of atoms, constantly vibrate, twist, turn, and wiggle. One of the properties that physicists have abstracted from their continuous motion is called 'spin.' Ingeniously designed experiments showed that spin interacted with external magnetic forces and that most subatomic particles possessed this property. At first (about 1927), spin was thought to be something like the spin of a top, but modern notions liken it to a fuzzy cloud or perhaps a fuzzy spinning doughnut.

Although the exact nature of electron spin is unknown, when it manifests on a large scale it is known as magnetism and appears as a force around a wire conducting a current or as a force present around natural iron ore called 'lodestone'.

THE 'SPINNING' ELECTRON
=
THE BASIC MAGNETIC PARTICLE

Magnetism is always

16

present around electrons. However, we don't sense it's existence until trillions of electrons are organized in a particular way so as to make it apparent. The illustration below shows in simplistic terms how magnetism appears on the macroscopic level from the organization of individual electrons.

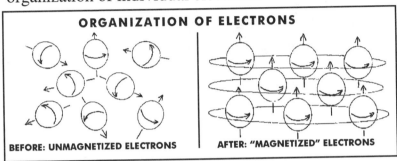

ORGANIZATION OF ELECTRONS

BEFORE: UNMAGNETIZED ELECTRONS   AFTER: "MAGNETIZED" ELECTRONS

Electrons in all matter, as well as by themselves, always exhibit the property called magnetism or spin, but only some electrons in some atoms can be organized and remain organized for any length of time. Of the 100 plus elements

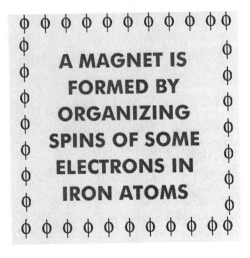

A MAGNET IS FORMED BY ORGANIZING SPINS OF SOME ELECTRONS IN IRON ATOMS

that have been discovered, only iron clearly shows a magnetic effect: that is, having organizable electrons. And only one or two electrons, out of the 26 electrons that make up an iron atom, are free to reorganize and stay organized long enough to produce the macroscopic effect we have called magnetism. Typically only 1 to 10 percent of the electrons in a permanent magnet are aligned. Just imagine what a strong magnet we would produce if all the electrons in iron atoms could be organized!

Contrary to popular belief, the magnetic force around iron does not spin around the poles.

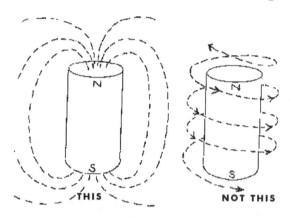

It is either directed into or out of the end or face as shown in this figure. The lines are abstractions that show the *constantly changing direction* of the force; they do not have any physical reality. Magnetic force doesn't travel around magnets, only the *direction* of force changes.

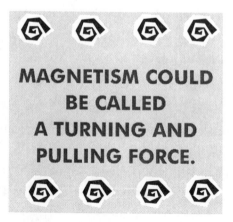

MAGNETISM COULD BE CALLED A TURNING AND PULLING FORCE.

If you bring a small magnet close to a larger one, it will first twist or turn so the smaller magnet has the same pole face up as the larger one, and then the small magnet will be pulled towards the larger one. Magnets or magnetic forces appear to have a circular, twisting, or spiraling effect on the path of moving electrons because their original motion combines with the magnetic force.

How electrons come to have this property called spin, or magnetism, remains as much of a puzzle as how they come to have a negative electrical charge. Magnetism still remains a mystery, although the frontier of the mystery has been pushed beyond the limits of our instrumental perception. Life is full of mysteries offering us a creative challenge which can motivate our scientific experiments.

MAGNETISM COULD ALSO BE CALLED AN ORGANIZING FORCE

In the next chapter the mystery of magnetic polarity will be carefully explained so you can understand how to use polarity in magnetic healing applications.

POLARITY AND STRENGTH

The terms 'polarity' and 'strength' confuse many people, partly because clear explanations about the fundamental nature of magnetism don't exist in the literature on biomagnetism, and partly because some writers use inappropriate terms. For example, the terms *'magnetic energy,' 'magnetic field,' 'magnetic waves' or 'magnetic current'* do not correspond to physical reality. Use of these terms can lead one astray from understanding the nature of magnetism.

The term 'polarity' **does** correspond to a physical property of every magnet. And it should be identified for optimum healing work. 'North' and 'south' have been historically used because it was found that a hanging or floating natural magnet would orient to Earth's north and south poles.

For healing work, all you really need to find is which side of your magnet to call south. Once you know that, you can mark it and you'll be in business. If you obtained a test magnet (commonly called a latch magnet) with this book that is painted red on the south side you can identify the polarity of any magnet. If you place the test magnet on any other magnet it

21

will flip around and stick with one color up. If red faces up, that identifies the red or south side of your test magnet. Mark at least one side of every magnet you have. Red nail polish or white-out may be used for this. You can paint a letter, 'N' or 'S', with such liquids, or you can attach a white label and mark it with a colored pen. If you don't have a test magnet you will need a compass and you can mark your magnets using it as a reference. The illustration on page 26 in this chapter will show you how to do this.

In addition to a test magnet, one of the most useful devices you can own for understanding the nature of magnetism is called a Magnaprobe[*]. It is like a little compass that is free to move in two dimensions with one end painted red and the other blue.

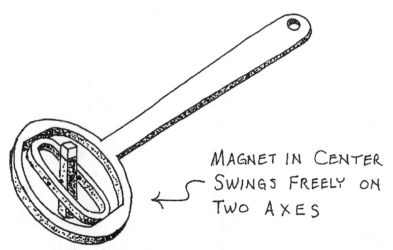

MAGNET IN CENTER
SWINGS FREELY ON
TWO AXES

MAGNAPROBE – Magnetic Force Direction Indicator.

---

[*] The Magnaprobe is available from PsychoPhysics Labs.

What happens when you move a Magnaprobe near a magnet? Initially, the free-swinging bar will turn, pointing one end toward the magnet. Then you will feel a pulling on the whole Magnaprobe. Magnetism, as a force, aligns other magnets and then pulls them close. The use of a Magnaprobe shows why magnetism may be called a "turning and pulling force."

Understanding the nature of magnetism allows us to place it in context with gravity and electricity.

GRAVITY   *- Pulls matter together.*

ELECTRICITY *- Pushes or pulls other particles.*

MAGNETISM   *- Twists then pulls other magnets.*

Another force was discovered in 1978 that is related to both gravity and magnetism. It is present around living organisms and is easily detected and measured with common household materials. The amplitude of rotation varies with changes in the activity of Earth's magnetic field. The direction of this spin force even reverses at the new and full moon or during strong magnetic disturbances. The existence of a spin force may be universal, a property of matter from electrons to galaxies. It has recently been postulated to exist around spinning bodies and a satellite is being launched to make measurements on it.[*]

---

[*] Science News, Nov. 15, 1997, Vol. 152, No. 21. American Journal of Acupuncture, December 1983. Chapter III of my book: *The Body Magnetic*.

COMPARISON OF FORCES
ELECTRIC & MAGNETIC CHARGES

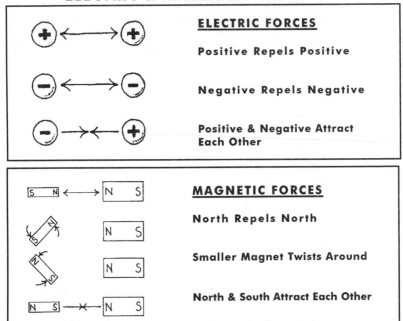

ELECTRIC FORCES

Positive Repels Positive

Negative Repels Negative

Positive & Negative Attract Each Other

MAGNETIC FORCES

North Repels North

Smaller Magnet Twists Around

North & South Attract Each Other

Of course, if two magnets happen to be already facing one another with unlike poles, only pulling happens. But if they are facing each other with like poles, then the smaller magnet will quickly, often quicker than the eye can follow, twist around so as to have its unlike pole face toward the larger magnet; then, if it's free to move, it will go towards the larger magnet.

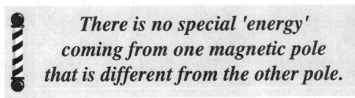

There is no special 'energy' coming from one magnetic pole that is different from the other pole.

The only difference between so-called "poles" is the *direction* of the magnetic force *at the surface of the magnet.* Thus, the word 'polarity' may be replaced by the phrase "magnetic force direction."

A short distance to the side the direction gradually changes from vertical to the magnetic pole face to horizontal, and then reverses at the opposite face.

If you determine the magnetic force direction by using a Magnaprobe, you will find that it quickly changes from pointing directly toward the face or end of a magnet to a horizontal direction. As you move the Magnaprobe around the magnet, you will see that the force *direction* curves around and reverses on the other side of the magnet.

Since polarity refers to a direction, not an innate property, all magnets have two poles, or directions, as well as all directions in between.

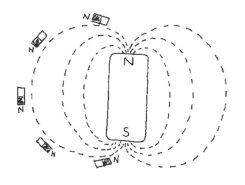

MAGNETIC FORCE DIRECTIONS

The term magnetic polarity came into use centuries before subatomic particles were discovered. After that (in the early 1900's) people naturally wanted to explain magnetism in terms of properties of subatomic particles. Around 1920 the notion of 'spin'

25

was proposed to account for magnetism and other observations about the behavior of subatomic particles (see next chapter).

This direction is either toward the face of the magnet, or away from it. That's all there is to the property called 'polarity'. It's no big mystery.

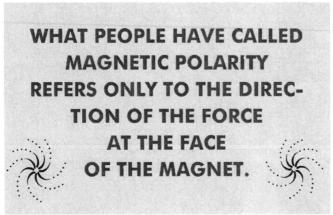

WHAT PEOPLE HAVE CALLED MAGNETIC POLARITY REFERS ONLY TO THE DIRECTION OF THE FORCE AT THE FACE OF THE MAGNET.

EARTH

BAR MAGNET

DEFINITION OF NORTH POLARITY

The Earth's magnetic poles are taken as the reference for all magnetic directions. To avoid confusion remember the following definition:

> *If the magnetic force at a magnet's surface is in the same direction as the magnetic force of Earth, that surface is said to be a north polarity.*

That is, the north pole of Earth and north pole of your magnet should both attract the same end of a compass needle. If you keep the previous illustration in mind and you use a test magnet or make your own, you won't get polarity mixed up.

Sometimes the terms **bionorth** and **biosouth** will be used in this book, where bio refers to biological north, as used in biomagnetic therapy. Physicists have historically used the opposite definition for polarity and this sometimes confuses people. And remember it's only a definition; completely arbitrary, nothing to argue about.

For biological use consider your magnet to be like a little Earth. If the same end of a compass needle that points to the north also points to a face of your magnet, that face can be defined as 'bionorth' in polarity. The other face, of course, will be 'biosouth.'

Please note that there is no 'current' that travels out of or into a magnet. The force does not travel. **No energy flows from one pole to the other or into your body when a magnet is placed on it.** It is only the *change in direction* of the magnetic force that forms a curve or arc around the magnet, and thus reverses on the opposite face. **The force itself does not curve.** The force is just an abstraction referring to the observed alignment of a free-swinging magnet at successive points around the magnet. If you get a Magnaprobe and play with it for a while you will get a clearer picture.

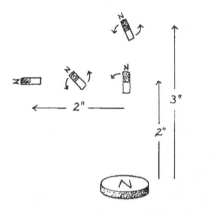

Various Distances
Indicator Magnet
Deflects From
Force of Powerful
Neodymium Magnet
(1 inch dia.)

CHANGING MAGNETIC FORCE DIRECTIONS ABOVE A NEODYMIUM MAGNET

Most magnets are manufactured to accentuate two magnetic force directions, usually called north and south, but in practice, "pure" north or south could only be applied to a part of the body if the treating magnet covered a larger area than the part being treated. For any typical magnet that might be used on the body, the force direction changes to horizontal (assuming the magnetic pole face is vertical) within 2 to 8 inches. Even the magnetic force from a one- inch diameter powerful neodymium magnet switches to horizontal a few inches away from dead center. It begins to turn downward only two inches directly away from, and two inches off center.

Manufacturers often mark magnets sold for biological research, either blue or green for bionorth, and red for biosouth. I recommend color coding all the magnets you have, or purchase, with red on the biosouth side and blue on the bionorth side.

Sometimes writers call the poles positive and negative. Since these terms are used for electricity and denote the flow of a current between them, I do not advise their use for magnetic poles. **Magnetic currents do not flow between north and south poles**. Use of such terms could unconsciously give a misleading idea to some people. The terms positive and negative also have connotations of good and bad, which may confuse users of magnets even more. Please avoid these terms also, along with 'magnetic energy', 'magnetic current', and 'magnetic power'.

If possible avoid the terms 'north seeking' and 'south seeking' as these too, only add more confusion to the terminology. We could call the poles black and white, yin and yang, or sweet and sour. The latter terms might be more appropriate since one magnetic force direction will sweeten fruit and the other will often make it less tasty. You can easily try this experiment. Use grapes that are still a bit unripe for a first experiment.

MAGNETIC STRENGTH, or pull, depends on how far a tiny magnet is from the larger one. Obviously if a test magnet is two feet away from a magnet, there won't be much pulling force. Therefore, it is defined only at the surface and measured in units called Gauss, after a German mathematician who lived about two hundred years ago. Unfortunately, Gauss is another misleading term that confuses people who use magnets for health, because it usually *refers to the strength right at the surface of the magnet.*

A tiny 3/16 inch disc magnet may have a stated gauss strength of 9,000 and a domino-size magnet a strength of only 850. However, the force of the domino magnet will extend 6 or 8 inches before diminishing to the strength of Earth's force (1 gauss). Whereas the force from a disc magnet drops to equal Earth's force less than two inches away. Most often, the Earth's force is

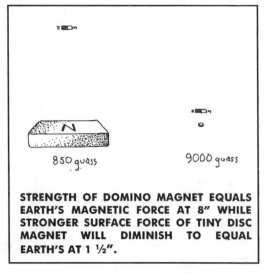

STRENGTH OF DOMINO MAGNET EQUALS EARTH'S MAGNETIC FORCE AT 8" WHILE STRONGER SURFACE FORCE OF TINY DISC MAGNET WILL DIMINISH TO EQUAL EARTH'S AT 1 ½".

considered to be about a gauss, but that is only at the surface of Earth, not the surface of the iron core within Earth which is supposedly the source of the magnetic force. Earth's core magnetic strength must be far more than one gauss!

For instance, if one hundred domino magnets are placed close together on the floor, Earth's magnetic force equals the force from those magnets at about waist height! To say Earth's strength is less than one gauss doesn't give a clear picture. I suspect that if the whole wall of of my office were plastered with domino magnets of 850 gauss strength each, the force at my desk eight feet away would still be less than the magnetic force of Earth. If an electromagnet consisting of a coil of wire was placed around the wall, the current would have to be several hundred amperes to equal Earth's field.

A more useful designation for magnets might be the gauss strength multiplied by the weight of the magnet, since most magnets are made of iron with a few additive metals.

A tiny but strong magnetic disc would have, for example, a gauss strength of 9,000 x .005 oz, or 45 whereas a domino magnet would have a gauss strength of 850 x 1.7 oz or 1,445 (see Chapter 7, p 69). A Magnetic Power Pad, 6 inches in diameter, has a' gauss-weight product of about 16,000. Earth's gauss-weight would be enormous by this measure.

Marketers of magnetic devices often advertise the magnetic gauss strength of their products, as if gauss strength were the most significant aspect of a magnet.

Obviously one needs a stronger and larger magnet to penetrate through a cast and treat a broken leg than what would be needed to treat a sore finger or stimulate the pancreas gland, but generally I have found that the primary direction, or "polarity," of the magnetic force is more important than its strength.

Chapter 4 describes some commonly available types of magnets and magnetic materials which biomagnetic therapists frequently use.

MAGNETIC MATERIALS AND TYPES

A wide range of magnetic materials, shapes, and strengths is available today, thanks to modern technology. I will describe some common magnetic materials and their properties to give you a basic overview of what's available.

TYPES OF MAGNETIC MATERIALS

Iron atoms have only one or two electrons that can be reoriented by an external magnetic force. Electrons in other types of atoms are fixed in their magnetic orientations. No other elements have electrons that can be affected by an external magnetic as easily as iron. Even the few electrons in iron that exhibit this flexibility will not retain it long. Heating iron metal or hitting it with a hammer a few times will 'demagnetize' it as the electrons will revert to random orientations again or line up with Earth's magnetic organizing force. Because of this, manufacturers usually add another element that not only makes the magnet 'permanent,' but also adds other special qualities, depending upon the element added. Elements most commonly used include nickel, barium, boron, cobalt, samarium, strontium, and neodymium.

The three main types of artificially-made, iron-based, permanent magnets are called 'alnico,' 'ferrite' (also called 'ceramic'), and 'rare earth.' The table below describes these types, the elements they contain, and the special features of each type.

TYPES OF ARTIFICIAL MAGNETS		
Iron	Soft Iron	The first type of permanent magnet made; much stronger than natural lodestone. But pure iron won't stay magnetized very long. Heating or dropping a magnetized iron bar will demagnetize it.
	Alnico	The first type of alloyed magnetic material. Alnico is made by mixing nickel and aluminum with iron. Alnico needs a "keeper" across the poles to retain its magnetism.
Ferrites (Ceramic)	Barium Ferrite	Barium combines with iron atoms to form barium ferrite, a stronger magnetic compound than alnico. It doesn't need to have a keeper, and can be powdered, melted, and cast into any desired shape or size, then magnetized. Barium ferrite magnets have been manufactured in the United States since 1954.
	Rubber Magnets	A flexible plastic material is mixed with powdered barium ferrite to produce a material that is fairly strong magnetically and won't break. It's usually magnetized in strips of alternating polarity.
	Strontium Ferrite	Strontium also combines chemically with iron to form a magnetic compound. Like barium, it can be powdered, and cast into different shapes. It is no longer used.
Rare Earth	Samarium-Cobalt	Samarium and cobalt can be mixed with pure iron to produce a very strong magnetic material. It, too, can be cast, but only produced in small sizes. It is expensive.
	Neodymium	The most recently discovered and most powerful type of magnet material is made by combining the rare earth element neodymium with iron and a little boron, a common element. Basic crystals in neodymium magnets are made out of 56 iron atoms, 8 neodymium atoms, and 4 boron atoms. This material can be cast and shaped in small sizes only. It is expensive.

Strontium ferrites, or ceramic magnets as they are often called, are the most common type of magnets available. They provide the most value for the money and are readily available in many different forms. These magnets can be made more powerful by making them larger. Their main disadvantage is that they are brittle and chip or break easily. Neodymium magnets were developed in the 1980s. They are much stronger than ceramic magnets and more expensive.

COMMON MAGNETIC SHAPES

Iron, mixed with other elements, can be melted and cast in practically any shape. Some of the more common and useful ones for biomagnetic therapy are described below.

MINIATURE MAGNETS

Powerful, thin disc magnets less than 1/4 inch in diameter are commonly used by acupuncturists. They often come in convenient packages of 5 or 10, with each magnet placed on a piece of circular sticky tape so it can be easily applied to an acupuncture point.

BLOCK MAGNETS

Big, heavy, and strong, block magnets are available in several different sizes. A common size is about 6 x 4 inches and 3/4 inches thick. With a gauss strength of one thousand, these ceramic magnets are useful for whole body treatments. Care must be taken in handling all magnets, but especially these because they are so powerful that they will pull other magnets to them hard enough to chip them. Two of these big magnets together can pinch fingers hard enough to break the skin. These magnets are brittle and break easily .

DOMINO MAGNETS

A little larger than a domino, these small black magnets are the most widely available and the least expensive for the magnetic force produced. They are often called 'Briggs and Stratton' magnets, after the two engineers who used them in the design of small gasoline motors.

COOKIE MAGNETS

These are flat discs about 1½ inches in diameter and 3/16 inches thick. Ideal for treating minor aches and pains, they cover a larger area than Domino magnets (1.8 square inches versus 1.3), although they are slightly weaker. Cookie magnets are easy to apply in pairs to the body. One can be placed inside clothing and one opposite it on the outside, holding each other in place. They are thin, lightweight, and unobtrusive.

DISC MAGNETS

In addition to cookie magnets, there are other disc magnets ranging from 1/4 inch diameter to over two inches in diameter with varying thickness.

LATCH MAGNETS

Latch magnets are used by the millions to close cupboard doors. They are flat rectangles about one inch square with a 1/8 inch hole in the center. The test magnet included with this book is an example of a latch magnet.

RING MAGNETS

Ring magnets, which are doughnut shaped, vary in size from about one inch in diameter to over six inches. Some are rings with a large central area, and others are discs with a small hole in the center. The magnetic force direction (or 'polarity') reverses sharply exactly at the center of the rings.

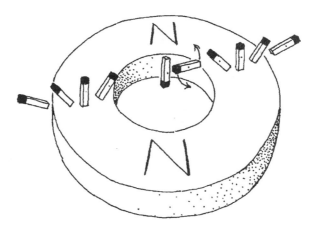

RING MAGNET SHOWING POLARITY REVERSAL AT EXACT CENTER

This characteristic creates a circular pattern of alternating polarity, which is useful in some applications.

CYLINDERS

Magnetized cylinders may be any size from 1/4 inch round and 1/4 inch long to over two inches round. Cylinders longer than about six inches will not be strongly magnetized at the ends.

ALTERNATING POLARITY MAGNETIC MATERIALS

By constructing special coils for use in the magnetizing process, ceramic magnetic material can be magnetized with two or more poles on the same face.

Sometimes these are called 'bipolar magnets,' although that is confusing since all magnets have two poles (or directions of force).

MULTIPOLE MAGNET

What is meant here is that the magnet has two poles on one face, instead of the usual single-pole face with bipolar ends. Multipole magnets is another term used by manufacturers sometimes referring generally to any magnet having more than one direction of force, on one face, but often referring specifically to magnets having three or more poles on the same face. Multipole magnets can be purchased as discs or foils.

SHEETS OR FOILS

These have flexible plastic combined with the powdered iron magnetic mixtures to provide large-area, low-gauss strength magnetism. They come in large sheets like cloth and can be cut according to need.

NEODYMIUM MAGNETS

(Pronounced Neo-de-me-um, called 'neos' for short)

These powerful and expensive magnets currently cannot be made much thicker than a half an inch or much wider than an inch. However, within that size restriction, discs, blocks, cylinders, and other shapes are available.

Neodymium magnets are especially worthwhile for applications where maximum force is required with minimum weight.

ELECTROMAGNETS

Coils of wire can be formed to practically any desired shape or size. Magnetic strength can be varied by increasing the current, up to the melting point of insulation.

Magnetic wave form and pulse rate can also be varied for experimental purposes. Electromagnets are fully discussed in my book called *Advanced Magnetic Therapy.*

Some common magnets are illustrated below. The weight, gauss strength, and gauss-weight product is also given.

TYPE OF MAGNET	Acu-puncture Magnet	Latch (test) Magnet	Small Ring Magnet	Cookie Magnet	Domino Magnet
VARIOUS MAGNETS AND THEIR WEIGHTS					
Magnets shown are approx. 1/3 actual size					
WEIGHT	.005 oz.	.3 oz	.7 oz.	1.9 oz.	1.7 oz.
GAUSS STRENGTH	9000	400	300	650	850
GAUSS X WEIGHT	45	120	210	1235	1450

The next chapter will describe how magnetic therapy companies have incorporated these basic types of magnetic materials into garments and devices.

CHAPTER 5

MAGNETIC GARMENTS & DEVICES

GARMENTS

Magnets have been placed in every possible garment from shoes to hats. You can buy magnetic garments or make your own. Garments made with rows of magnets alternating in polarity are commonly made in the orient and imported in this country. Magnetic garments made in the United States often consist of domino magnets sewn between layers of cloth, although one manufacturer only uses ring magnets. Such garments are heavy but they work well on many common ailments. Other garments are made from sections of thin flexible magnetic material, usually alternating in polarity, in the form of strips, rings, or a checkerboard pattern. Many garments are made with only bionorth towards the body with no possibility of reversing the polarity; whereas others can be easily reversed.

The garments with thin rubber-like magnetic materials don't have as much penetrating power as garments made with domino or ring magnets. However as I've written before, bigger is not necessarily better. Low strength magnetic forces can be sufficient to alter the blood chemistry as it flows past them, and that in turn can affect conditions within the body some distance away. Such garments or patches can also help surface wounds heal when taped directly over the wound. Low gauss magnets may be sufficient to stimulate acupuncture points when placed at the appropriate places in the body.

Garments with larger, stronger magnets may be more useful for releasing muscle cramps, speeding healing of broken bones, stimulating or sedating organs, or restoring nerve functioning.

If you are considering the purchase of magnetic garments it's wise to choose those that have the capability of being worn with either polarity toward the body, or that have pockets allowing you to reverse the polarity direction at will. Of course, if you purchase garments with alternating polarity, reversibility won't be needed. Prices vary widely: shop around before investing a lot of money. If you have time and sewing skills you can try making your own garments.

COMMONLY AVAILABLE MAGNETIC GARMENTS

shoe inserts	necklaces
knee wraps	pendants
back supports	face masks
neck & shoulder wraps	head bands
bracelets	

COMMENTS ABOUT EACH TYPE

Shoe inserts are thin pads usually made by placing 15 to 20 1/4 inch diameter discs in the pad. Usually the magnets have the north poles towards the body, although when I checked a pair with a test magnet, I found a couple of the tiny discs were reversed. Ideally shoe inserts ought to be reversible so individual needs or differences can be taken into account. Some shoe inserts are also made of alternating polarity flexible rubber material. This eliminates the possibility of manufacturing error or uncertainty about which polarity to use on which foot and may work well enough for ordinary conditions.

Some people have received remarkable benefits by using shoe inserts. It seems like people who have to stand all day or have foot problems would be good candidates for this type of device.

Knee wraps can be beneficial for many: e.g. athletes who use their knees actively, hikers, bikers, or older people whose gait has become unsteady. A lot of blood flows through the legs and any magnetic polarity, or strength would be far better than none. Also, since knee wraps add some mechanical support to the

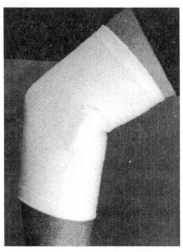

KNEE WRAP

43

knee, they feel good to wear. I found the best kind are those which are whole elastic sleeves that you have to slip your foot into and slide them up to the knee. The types that attach by velcro often come off the knees if one is actively moving around. Sleeves can usually be reversed to direct more of the opposite force into the body.

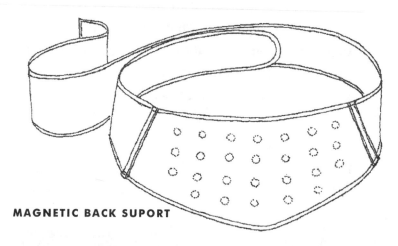

MAGNETIC BACK SUPORT

Back supports are wonderful! They help tone the body, improve circulation, and help some types of back problems quite well. The type drawn above has about 20 magnetic discs about 3/8 inches in diameter. A velcro strip holds the band firmly in place. It can be reversed to provide either bionorth or biosouth towards the body. For my secretary and me biosouth is the preferred direction.

Another useful type of magnetic back device is simply a pad about the size of a large hand. Alternating strips of flexible magnetic material eliminate the need for determining polarity. The thin pad can be readily slipped into the waist line under a shirt.

Some back pains may be related to knee or foot misalignments, kidney or liver problems, or carrying too much weight in the belly, thereby constantly straining the muscles. If magnetic treatments don't help a back problem within a week, check for problems elsewhere in the body.

Neck and shoulder wraps can be worn while working or driving. The type illustrated in the photo is made of domino magnets fastened between two layers of cloth. Although fairly heavy, it feels good on the neck.

MAGNETIC NECK WRAP

Serious wrist injuries or conditions may be treated by *magnetic wrist wraps*. You can make your own

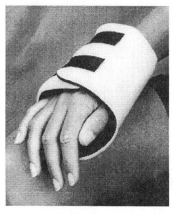

MAGNETIC WRIST WRAP

with test magnets or domino magnets if you are handy with sewing materials. I have used wrist wraps, with magnets smaller than test magnets, as I type. There is no need to worry about erasing computer hard drives or discs at that distance. Such small magnets will erase credit cards, however.

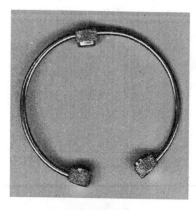

MAGNETIC BRACELET

Bracelets come in several varieties. One type is like a watch band, with magnets about half the size and thickness of test magnets, alternating in polarity between sections of flexible chain-like material. Other types have 1/4 inch diameter flex magnets placed at two or three spots on a stiff metal rod which can be bent open to accommodate larger wrists.

MAGNETIC NECKLACE

Necklaces also come in several varieties. The one I like consists of slim cylindrical gold plated magnets about 1/2 inch long. This definitely works; I'm often wearing one as I write.

Other types of necklaces consist of shiny black hematite (iron ore) beads, rhodium plated cylinders, or plated disc magnets. Most necklaces have alternating polarity forces.

Magnet pendants are also available in different styles since they are basically just magnets hung around the neck by a chain, string, or leather strip. You can easily make one by hanging the test magnet from a string since it has a convenient hole available. Experiment. See which polarity feels best for you.

MAGNETIC PEN-

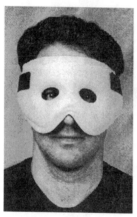

MAGNETIC FACE-

Halloween or not, a *face mask* may help you get rid of wrinkles. Before and after photos have been published which show excellent results. I intend to try a magnetic face mask after getting a few more wrinkles from writing this book and hours of peering at words on screens.

Magnetic headbands can help some types of headaches disappear in minutes. They may also help people recover quicker from hangovers. You can readily make your own from ring magnets, flexible rubber magnetic chunks, or any other small magnets. When using magnets around the head be careful; a slight headache can be produced by using the wrong polarity or too strong a magnet.

Beanies have not yet made their appearance on the magnetic garment market to my knowledge. However they would probably be helpful for occasional stimulation or sedation of the pineal gland.

PRODUCTS

Magnetic Power Pads™ are six inch diameter encapsulated magnets for use in the kitchen, office, or bedroom. Blue plastic on one side and red on the other makes polarity identification easy. Used for treating water, increasing plant growth, sweetening fruit, putting under the mattress, feet, or buttocks, they are handy to have around.

MAGNETIC POWER

Magnetic car seats are made by several companies. Magnets placed in foam materials can be helpful to improve circulation and reduce aches and pains for those who have to spend much time in the car. Magnetic car seats are great for long trips. Magnetic treatments won't substitute for exercise though. The body depends on exercise to maintain the circulation of blood in the legs and the lymph fluid all throughout the body.

Magnetic Beds come in many shapes and sizes. There are thin pads that you can carry with you, thick, heavy, queen size magnetic mattresses with down covers that also have tiny magnets imbedded in them, and even magnetic pads for your cat, dog, or horse. I haven't seen any magnet pads for gold fish yet; perhaps the market's too small.

Many magnetic beds are made with domino magnets placed between layers of foam. Some beds are made with ring magnets or small multipolar disc magnets. It may be desirable to have a magnetic bed that can be turned over to experience the opposite magnetic polarity if your body needs that at a given time. It's a good idea to check polarity with a Magnaprobe, test magnet, or compass. Magnetic polarities cannot be seen and people easily can make mistakes. Prices and quality varies, so shop around. Dr. John Zimmerman, Director of The Bioelectric Magnetic Institute, in Reno, Nevada, has compared a number of magnetic beds (see Chapter 10).

MAGNETIC BED MADE OF MAGNETIC POWER

A simple do-it -yourself bed can be made from 8-12 Magnetic Power Pads placed under the mattress. They should be at least four inches away from the body to smooth out the magnetic force. Polarity can be varied by placing individual power pads with the north or south side up as you choose. For instance you might have north pole under your head area to sleep more, and south pole under your back to stimulate healing, north pole under knees, and south pole under the feet if you happen to have a little arthritis there. Or you can alternate polarity magnet by magnet or day by day. You can also purchase domino magnets from an industrial supplier and make your own magnetic pads.

To treat the whole body with one magnetic polarity would require a single magnetic slab larger than your bed. All beds made with permanent magnets will produce horizontal force directions a few inches above the magnets; that is, right in the center of your body.

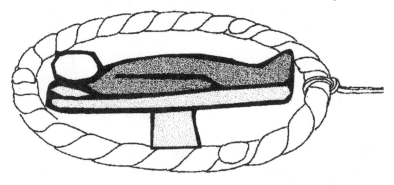

The electromagnetic bed which I use consists of a coil which circles the entire bed and pulses at the frequency and polarity of my choice. By this means it's possible to obtain a more homogeneous magnetic force.[*]

Many people report excellent effects from magnetic beds, others say they are irritating. It seems to be dif-

---

[*] Custom designed beds and other devices which produce pulsating magnetic fields can be ordered from PsychoPhysics Labs.

ferent for different people. Before spending a lot of money on a magnetic bed, it might be wise to try one for a few days. It may not be necessary to sleep on a magnetic bed every night.

For a while I had a *magnetic toothbrush.* The manufacturer cited informal research data showing a reduction in gum diseases when the toothbrush was used. Two companies sell *magnetic water picks.* The one I have has two tiny magnets across from one another on the small tube which goes from the pump to the nozzle. The magnets are of opposing polarities. A study has been published in the Journal of Clinical Periodontology (see references, Chapter 10), I glued three domino magnets on the water holder of mine to increase the magnetic effect. I also frequently suck on a small magnet about the size of a pencil eraser. I can't tell if it has any value, but my mouth does feel cleaner after rolling it around in my teeth for a while.

I also have a *magnetic juicer* which has small magnets inbedded in it to improve the quality of the juice. Probably the magnetic effect can be increased by placing the juices on a large magnet until they are consumed. Clearly these pioneering technologies will someday probably be commonplace around the home.

WHAT ELSE?

Any product you can think of may be enhanced by magnetic forces. People use magnets on gas lines, the water hose for cars, water pipes for houses, in their hot tubs, swimming pools, bath tubs, dishwasher, washing machine, and probably even the toilet tank. While magnets may improve these functions or uses, it's often difficult to prove benefits. In order to ascertain whether or not magnetic forces could improve fuel efficiency, I wanted to set up a gasoline lawn mower on a test stand and supply it with a specific amount of gasoline, time the duration of running, then repeat the test again when magnets were applied to the gasoline. But even this simple test didn't work well because variability in starting the motor could not be controlled.

If you make your own devices, using domino magnets, you may have some positive results. Perhaps you will come up with a novel product.

HOW MAGNETS WORK

There are many ways that magnetism works in the body to help it heal. Several different body structure levels can be defined starting at the largest physical level and working downward in size. These are: the body as a whole, muscles, organs, glands, circulatory systems, nervous system, acupuncture meridians, cells, molecules, atoms, and protons and electrons. Studies are always underway on how the fascinating force of magnetism assists the healing process.

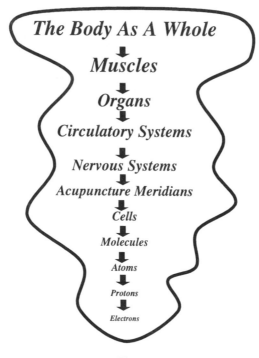

The Body As A Whole
⬇
Muscles
⬇
Organs
⬇
Circulatory Systems
⬇
Nervous Systems
⬇
Acupuncture Meridians
⬇
Cells
⬇
Molecules
⬇
Atoms
⬇
Protons
⬇
Electrons

To do a comprehensive study of anything takes time and careful analysis. Money to support people and purchase instruments for making measurements may not be easily obtained. Therefore there are more anecdotal reports than formal studies. A few mechanisms that have been studied and published in the scientific literature include:

1. Increase in blood flow and oxygen absorption by the tissues.
2. Change in hormone secretions.
3. Increase in cell division rate.
4. Increase in enzyme activity.
5. Regeneration of nerve tissue.
6. Healing of bone fractures.

I will discuss each structural level in turn. Please understand that there is more material available than is briefly summarized in this book.

At the whole-body level, I have observed a change in an aspect of the human aura that I have called the biofield. As mentioned on page 27, this field is easy to detect and measure and it's variations can be easily verified by anyone but formal research has not yet been done.

At the muscular level, people commonly get stiff muscles, strained muscles, or muscle cramps. All of these have been helped by magnetic therapy, although the only formal study I've seen has been on stiff necks by TDK, the Japanese company which manufactures magnetic tape. TDK also makes a magnetic necklace.

They asked for feedback from several thousand of the several million users. Seventy nine percent reported the necklaces were highly effective after the third or fourth day of use. I noticed the same thing. The effect could be from increased blood flow.

> *Increased blood flow and increased oxygen absorption are probably the most important factors in magnetic treatment.*

The healing process speeds up when more blood carries nutrients and oxygen to the cells. One careful series of studies was done in Germany by Dr. Ulrich Warnke, and another series was done independently at Loma Linda University in California by Dr. Benjamin Lau. Blood flow was found to increase by a factor of two or more, although the exact mechanism is still unknown. There may be more than one. Vasodilatation of capillaries is believed to be a factor. When red blood cells are examined under a microscope they are often clumped together in the blood of people with ailments. With a magnetic treatment, the red blood cells disperse, allowing more oxygen transfer from the lungs and to the cells. This cannot be due to magnetic effects on the iron, because the iron in hemoglobin is chemically bound, so the electrons are not free to change their orientation under the influence of an external magnetic field.

Contrary to popular belief, blood cells do not line up under the influence of a magnetic field. If they were magnetic, they could be stopped from flowing by placing a strong magnet on the body! In fact, just the opposite seems to happen: Blood flows more readily and blood cells disperse, thereby enhancing oxygen transfer from the blood to the tissues of the body. Dr. Linus Pauling won a Nobel prize for his work on the effect of magnetic forces on hemoglobin and its ability to carry oxygen. Pauling found the effects were complicated. More informally, I personally noticed the effect of magnetism on oxygen when I pretreated myself before climbing and skiing at high altitudes and found no high-altitude effects. I also noticed similar improvement in performance when I treated my chest before going for a jog.

Increased healing of bones has been studied and reported in standard medical journals by A.L. Bassett, M.D. and his colleagues. Only one of his many articles is listed in the reference section; the interested reader can track others. Dr. Bassett also wrote one article on nerve regeneration in rats. Richard Hopkins, a biomagnetic therapist in San Diego, is working with spinal cord regeneration cases. He has helped several people to regain some muscular control using his special magnets.

The endocrine system of glands is basic to good functioning of the body. Drs. Richard and Mary Broeringmeyer, pioneers in magnetic therapy, have long observed that glandular secretions can be either increased or decreased by magnetic forces of either south or north polarity. This is a difficult topic to research formally, but there is one report of increased hormone production from the pineal gland (see references in Chapter 10). Males are invited to experiment on themselves to see if testosterone seems to increase as evidenced by increased sexual desire. I did notice such an effect using pulsed magnetic fields.

Davis reported that rats exposed to strong south pole magnetic forces lived longer only if they were not allowed to copulate. The cycles of warring behavior described in Chapter 1 may be triggered by solar geomagnetic activity inducing increased testosterone in males. If so, the adage of the 60's, "Make love, not war," may be supported by biochemistry as well as psychology.

You can find descriptions of more laboratory studies described in books listed in the references section. Research is ongoing at universities such as the University of Washington (multiple sclerosis), Loma Linda University (Parkinson's disease), the University of Virginia (bedsores), and Leeds University. New benefits are being discovered every year. Articles on magnetism and biological systems, specifically conditions such as bone healing, Parkinson's disease, and head injuries, now appear regularly in major medical journals. Typical journal articles are listed in Chapter 10.

Wound healing has been reported to speed up by magnetic therapy, and reduction of scar tissue formation has been observed. I noticed this when I taped a small magnet to big cuts on myself and my eight year old son from time to time. When I recently tore a nickel-sized chunk of skin off my foot it was painful for a couple of days. I then taped a small disc magnet directly on the wound overnight and was amazed at how quickly the wound healed and how smooth the skin was directly under the magnet. A month later I could not even be sure of the spot that was injured! Magnetic forces seem to help organize cell formation. This could be a general and important principle of magnetic healing, along with increased blood flow and increased oxygen adsorption.

Plants, as well as other organisms, are clearly affected by magnetic forces. Working independently, researchers in several countries outside the United States have found significantly increased plant growth when the seeds are pretreated, the plants are exposed while growing or the water given to the plants is treated. Three articles are listed in the references; one by a Canadian researcher, one by a German, and one by an Israeli. It's pretty easy to experiment with magnets on plants in your own home or backyard.

On the next page is a photo of flowers placed over Magnetic Power Pads after a month of growing. The magnetically treated plants grew twice as fast as the untreated ones. I expected this result from reading the literature, but wanted to verify it myself, which you also may wish to do. I found similar results with wheat sprouts, sunflowers, and impatiens flowers.

PHOTO **OF PLANT GROWTH WITH AND WITHOUT MAGNETIC TREATMENT**

Clearly, magnetic forces alter the biochemistry of plants. If the polarity and strength are correct, the results are often dramatic. Since magnetism works so well for plants it seems reasonable that magnetism would work for people too.

Although plants and people differ, one element in common to their biochemistry is water. Others have said the acidity of water could be altered by magnetic treatment. However, when I obtained a sensitive pH or acidity-testing instrument, I found that magnetic treatment did not produce any changes in the acidity of tap water, distilled water, or fruit juices. I experimented with different strengths of permanent magnets as well as pulsing magnets. There were changes in these liquids if they were left sitting overnight (no magnetic treatments). Whatever the mechanism, it's clear that biosouth pole treatment makes water taste better and sweetens fruit, according to most adults.

You might try placing a bunch of grapes (not quite ripe) on one large magnet and a similar bunch of grapes on a twin magnet with the opposite pole face. And of course, a third bunch of grapes left untreated as a control. At different times taste one or two grapes from each bunch. You can extend the test from ½ hour to a day or two. Do the same with water. Ask others to also taste the substances treated. Plants watered with biosouth-treated water grow faster than non-treated plants.

"PERHAPS I CAN SWEETEN HIM TOO!"

A definite change in the ultraviolet transmission of biosouth treated water compared with bionorth treated water was observed by biochemist, Dr. Glen Rein. He inferred that this was due to a change in the amount of dissolved oxygen compared to control samples. Perhaps it is this factor that accounts for the taste difference and the observed difference in the growth of plants.

At the **subatomic level**, some electrons and some protons can be twisted slightly by a magnetic force, even though they cannot be completely turned around. (They definitely can't jump out of an atom and leap to a magnet!) Their freedom of movement may be analogous to a Magnaprobe with it's little bar magnet that is only free to swivel in two directions, or a compass needle that can only swing in one dimension. Neither the compass needle nor the tiny bar magnet can escape; they can only twist and turn, no matter how strong the applied magnetic force.

MRI, or Magnetic Resonance Imaging, depends on the fact that some protons in hydrogen atoms, carbon atoms, oxygen atoms, and sodium atoms will twist slightly when an external magnetic is applied. When the magnetic force is removed, these protons emit minute, low-frequency radio waves that can be detected by sensitive radio frequency amplifiers and computer processed to produce 'pictures.'

Could minute radio waves emitted by twisting protons play a part in chemical and molecular reactions which go on continuously within a living organism? If so, we have a definite mechanism for exploring how magnets work. Such a mechanism might also account for how sound therapy works as well, since the proton frequencies induced by magnetic forces can be in the audible range at times.

Since it is the change in magnetic force as well as the absolute value of the magnetic strength that produces a twist in protons, ring magnets, alternating field magnets, and pulsing electromagnets could be more effective than block magnets for some conditions. This topic is worth serious research.

Blood and lymph, being composed largely of water, have plenty of hydrogen atoms combined with other atoms. Both fluids circulate continuously throughout the body, so the hydrogen protons would move in and out of the magnetic force of any magnet that was placed on a region of the body.

The protons twist slightly as they enter the region of the external magnetic force, then relax back to their original positions as they leave.

In the process of returning to their original positions they produce a small radio wave.

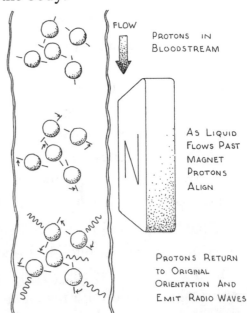

FLOW

PROTONS IN BLOODSTREAM

AS LIQUID FLOWS PAST MAGNET PROTONS ALIGN

PROTONS RETURN TO ORIGINAL ORIENTATION AND EMIT RADIO WAVES

PROTONS IN BLOOD MOVING BY MAGNET

How does tweaking hydrogen protons and the resulting generation of minute radio waves lead to alterations at the molecular level? It could be through effects on hydrogen bonding. The weak attraction for hydrogen atoms for one another is basic to biological organisms. Water molecules form different structures due to hydrogen bonding; the construction of DNA strings is based on hydrogen bonds between proteins. Other complex molecules also form structures based on this important linking process.[*]

Magnetic forces also seem to help organize things. If cells are disorganized from some ailment or accident, a magnet can apparently help the body reorganize them. Whether this is by the DNA hydrogen bonding mechanism, the water bonding mechanism, or some unknown (to me) lattice structure change in complex molecules, it does seem to happen. The exact mechanism will probably remain a mystery for some time.

You can read technical articles and anecdotal reports for months, but ultimately you need to try magnets for yourself. No book or article will guarantee that they will help you. You are unique. Fortunately, you don't have to wait for the answers before using magnets to improve your health.

---

[*] Electrons also produce minute signals when an external magnetic force of around 3,000 gauss is applied. The frequencies produced are in the microwave and infrared regions

The next chapter describes some typical magnetic materials that are now available for easy use in magnetic therapy.

CHAPTER 7

WHAT TO TREAT AND HOW TO TREAT IT

Since magnetic forces increase blood flow, they can be helpful for nearly any ailment or condition. Magnetism often dramatically helps acute injuries and, over time, chronic illnesses, although during treatment it seems that nothing is happening. Harmful effects are very rare and usually disappear immediately as soon as the magnetic polarity is reversed or use is discontinued. There are formal and informal studies and anecdotal reports on nearly every ailment. A list of common health problems treatable with magnetism follows.

CONDITIONS TREATED WITH MAGNETISM
Indicates I've had personal positive experience with it.

acute injuries*	cholesterol, high	migraines*
adrenal insufficiency	chronic fatigue syn.*	multiple sclerosis
allergies	constipation*	operation recovery
anxiety*	diabetes	pancreas insuff.*
arteriosclerosis	eye problems*	prostate enlgmt.
arthritis*	fractures*	seizures
asthma*	headaches*	shoulder pain*
back pain*	hemorrhoids*	sinus*
bladder weakness	hypertension	sore muscles*
brain injuries	insomnia	stomach upsets*
burns	kidney problems	tennis elbow*
cancer	knee pains*	tooth problems*
carpal tunnel	liver disease	ulcers
cataracts	menstrual cramps*	whiplash

Dr. William Philpott reported that some mental problems were quickly helped by applying bionorth polarity to the head. If this can be validated by other biomagnetic therapists it could be a major discovery.

Of course there is a placebo effect. This has been studied by TDK, the Japanese manufacturer of magnetic cassette tapes, which also makes biomagnetic devices. They found the placebo effect to be about 13%, meaning an improvement of about that much in symptoms using no actual magnetic forces, just dummy magnets. So you might as well *believe in the power of magnets to heal and add to your improvement rate when using real magnets.*

Positive beliefs help the healing process no matter what the condition or the treatment and such beliefs can be reinforced by the process of hypnosis. **Hypnosis works!** No doubt about it. As a practicing hypnotist for many years I can attest to its validity.[*] Anyone with any ailment or difficult health condition will probably benefit from the practice of hypnosis along with magnetic therapy, herbs, medicine, or whatever else seems appropriate. A good hypnotist can also help uncover any unconscious interfering beliefs as well as accentuating the positive ones.

---

[*] Hypnosis, meditation, and biofeedback can be combined in a synergistic manner for more effective results. See my book: *BIOMEDITATION* (Chapter 10) which also has several paper and pencil ways to bring out interfering beliefs.

SELECTION OF MAGNETS

Any magnet will probably be much better than no magnet. With the test magnet you can find the polarity of every magnet. If use of the test magnet seems ambiguous, the unknown magnet is probably a multipole magnet. All magnets you have should be tested and marked for polarity.

GENERAL PRINCIPLES OF TREATMENT
(not the ultimate truth)

Magnetic therapy is very simple as I stated in the first two pages of this book. Those guidelines are repeated below.

Basic Steps

1. Place a magnet on the area of injury, pain, or illness. Be quiet, focus inward, and notice if it feels better, worse, or no different.

2. If it feels worse, turn the magnet over.

3. If it feels better keep using it.

4. If there is no noticeable difference, leave the magnet in place for ten to fifteen minutes. Repeat, with the magnet in the same place facing the same way, two or three times a day for a few days.

5. If there is no improvement by that time, turn the magnet over and continue its application for a few more days.

6. If you don't notice any improvement within ten days, then magnets probably won't help. They won't hurt either.

The first step is to place a magnet directly on the site of the problem. Determine the polarity by the guidelines above or follow your intuition. In general, if there is acute pain and inflammation, use the bionorth polarity for a few days, then switch to the biosouth polarity to promote faster healing. If the condition has been present for a while or is chronic, use the biosouth polarity to begin with.

You can also try magnetic pads or devices with alternating polarity to see if they produce relief. Alternating polarity devices may be slower, at least for injuries involving a large region of the body, but can take the uncertainty out of which polarity to use.

If any irritation or pain increases when you apply a magnet, it will usually go away if you turn the magnet over for a few minutes or discontinue using them. However all magnetic therapists agree that tumors, cysts, or abnormal cell growths should be only treated with the north polarity because of a possible risk of stimulating tumor cell growth.

Obviously a larger injury should be treated with a larger magnet. In general, it's not a good idea to use large strong magnets on sensitive areas of the body such as the head, eyes, or heart, or leave even moderate size or strength magnets on such places for long periods of time, e. g. sleeping with them on or near by. It probably won't hurt, but it could temporarily unbalance the body chemistry. I've tried them with no adverse effects, but I'm not especially sensitive to magnetic forces or other noxious stimuli, and my health is usually in balance.

A magnet with a large surface area will naturally provide a more uniform north or south direction, if that seems important, whereas a tiny neo with a much stronger gauss strength at the surface will be exerting a horizontal force an inch or two away from the magnet. The illustration here shows at what distance the force from a domino magnet becomes equal

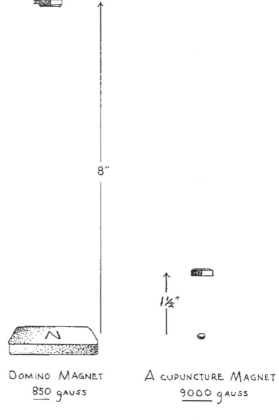

DOMINO MAGNET
850 gAUSS

A CUPUNCTURE MAGNET
9000 gAUSS

COMPARISON BETWEEN DOMINO MAGNET AND ACUPUNCTURE MAGNET

69

to that of the Earth compared with the distance that the force from an acupuncture magnet equals that of Earth.

Even though the acupuncture magnet has a rated gauss strength more than ten times that of the domino magnet, it does not penetrate nearly as far into the body. The illustration shows the magnets placed flat. When a domino magnet is placed sideways, the point where the Earth's field equals the strength of the domino magnet is about ten inches rather than eight inches. The following illustration shows comparable distances for a test magnet.

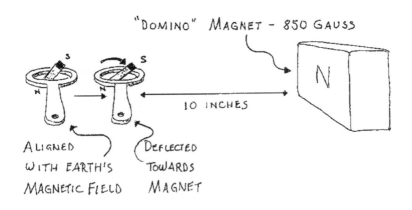

STRENGTH OF DOMINO MAGNET DIMINISHES TO EQUAL EARTH'S STRENGTH AT 10 INCHES

These illustrations were made by using a Magnaprobe as described in Chapter 3.

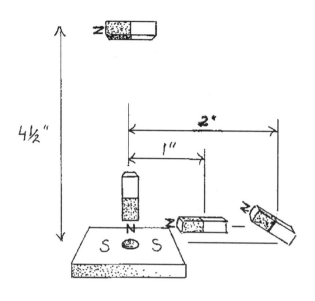

**MAGNETIC FORCE FROM TEST MAGNET EQUALS
EARTH'S FORCE FOUR INCHES ABOVE IT.**

A uniformly bionorth or biosouth force cannot not be obtained unless the magnet is about 1 ½ times as large in area as the region being treated. A permanent magnet of large size (more than four by six inches) is expensive, but coils can be made any size. I've made a coil to go around a whole wall, powered by a small car battery, pulsating at low frequencies. Bigger is not necessarily better. The body normally responds to very small magnetic forces (less than a thousandth of a gauss).

A small wound can be treated by taping the test magnet directly over it for a few hours or even over-night. The cells of the body are sensitive to magnetic

71

fields of hundredths of a gauss. Big strong magnets are best used for long periods on broken bones. Many studies have been published for this application and the FDA has approved magnetic treatments for fractures. In general, bone healing is speeded by a factor of two.

Acupuncturists use tiny, ¼ inch in diameter, disc magnets to stimulate acupuncture points. By placing small magnets precisely on the meridians, an acupuncturist can skillfully stimulate or sedate appropriate glands or organs even though the magnetic forces from such tiny magnets do not penetrate the entire body. See Holger Hannemann or Michael Tierra's books for details. Specific sites to apply alternating magnetic polarity pads for general treatments are clearly illustrated in chapter 10 of Allen Walls' book.

Generally, magnetic treatments can be applied anywhere on the body. Magnetic beds can be helpful for over all body treatment to increase flexibility, reduce neck, shoulder, or back pain, or enhance sleep. But if a person has a unique ailment, a more specific magnetic diagnosis may be more effective.

Glands and organs may benefit from different magnetic polarities, and treating with just one polarity all over the body would not be appropriate. Each organ or gland needs to be individually diagnosed and treated as called for.

For example, people with Chronic Fatigue Syndrome invariably are off on every gland and organ, but in different ways. That is, one gland will be overactive and the next one underactive. One gland will be helped by bionorth polarity and the other by biosouth. Treating both with just one primary polarity (which a magnetic bed produces - usually north) will probably not be as helpful as using the appropriate polarity. Moreover, it is not desirable to treat the body all the time with magnetic forces. The body adapts; magnets, like other medicines or treatments, can become ineffective if used continuously.

Sensitive people will often feel tingling sensations throughout the body or along acupuncture meridians when a magnet is first applied to the site of the injury. When people report this I take it as a good sign and know that magnetic treatment will likely produce good results.

If the above procedures don't help, or don't help quickly, you can apply magnets to related glands and organs. For example, infections may be helped by treating the thymus gland with the south polarity, to speed up the immune system, or the liver with the south polarity to speed up its action of filtering toxins from the body. The colon may be stimulated by treating with the biosouth polarity to help eliminate wastes, and the general heart area can be stimulated by biosouth to help increase blood flow and adsorbed oxygen.

General treatment on the feet (see Chapter 9) may help tonify the entire body, and treatment of the kidney (biosouth) may also help eliminate waste products.[*]

Sometimes a particular injury will also happen to be directly on a particular acupuncture meridian. It's possible then, for glands and organs related to that meridian to be affected. For example, I broke my collar bone. Acupuncture meridians for the colon are in that area and subsequently I developed a blocked colon. But treating the colon was not the answer - I needed to treat the collar bone.

WHICH POLARITY SHOULD BE USED?

There has often been confusion and even heated debate over which polarity to use. Much of this confusion appears to arise from a misunderstanding of the precise nature of magnetism. As described in Chapter 3, the difference between north and south polarity is not due to some special, unique, magical, or mysterious property; it is simply the primary direction of magnetic force at the surface of the

---

[*] For more detailed information on magnetic therapy for glands and organs see the book: Energy Medicine by Drs. Richard and Mary Broeringmeyer - Chapter 10

magnet. Since the direction of the force continually changes in a circular fashion around a magnet anyway, talking about north or south polarity is only talking about one portion of a curve (see illustration below).

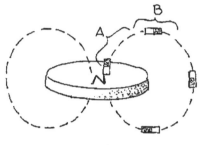

OBLIQUE SIDE VIEW

AREA A –   REGION OF MAXIMUM VERTICAL FORCE.

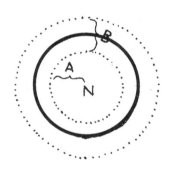

VIEW OF NORTH FACE

AREA B -   REGION OF MAXIMUM HORIZONTAL FORCE FOR COOKIE MAGNET.

TINY MAGNET IN VARIOUS POSITIONS AROUND A COOKIE MAGNET.

Since the force direction becomes horizontal an inch or so away from all but the largest magnets, it may not make that much difference which polarity is used when low strength or small area magnets are used. Nevertheless, differences in biological activity between the use of a north or south pole magnet are observed. Such differences were noted in the 1700's.

In the 30's Albert Davis rediscovered this difference and made a few more careful laboratory studies. Repeating many experiments over the years, he concluded that the biosouth polarity increased biological activity and the bionorth decreased it.

As stated in Chapter 3, I observed (and so did at least two others who published their research) that plants grew faster and taller when predominately exposed to the south polarity, but the north polarity also produced much greater growth than no magnetism at all. That may be why alternating polarity devices help the body heal about as well as north and south polarities. Only the treatment time may differ.

You may want to experimentfor yourself regarding this matter.

I've observed that sometimes healing does not occur if only the bionorth pole is used.

The use of alternating polarity garments or pads bypasses the question of which pole to use, although the use of one particular pole might work better in situations where a stronger magnetic force is called for, such as broken bones. I have not seen comparative studies. Only two reports have crossed my desk comparing alternating versus single pole treatments. Both studies stated that unipolar treatments worked faster than alternating, though any magnetic treatment was better than no treatment at all. I know of no studies on alternating polarity and plant growth and haven't gotten around to making my own tests. This would be a good experiment for an amateur scientist, a high school science fair project, a college student project, or even a Ph.D. thesis.

Ultimately any person using magnets must determine whether or not one polarity or the other or both simultaneously is actually helping the condition. A sensitive person will often know this within a few minutes.

MUSCLE TESTING

To obtain more certainty about which polarity to use, one can muscle test (sometimes called arm testing or applied kinesiology) then treat with the polarity that strengthens the body. Any muscle can be tested and it will be weaker or stronger when a magnet is applied to any part of the body, if that part, gland, or organ, is out of order and will respond to magnetic treatment. Generally if there is no noticeable difference, magnetic treatment will not be that helpful.

For those readers who are not familiar with this method, a description can be found in the author's other books on magnetism (see references) or by asking local health practitioners. Although I was initially skeptical about the use of muscle testing for determining which magnetic force direction to use, after fifteen years I've come to accept its validity[*].

ELECTROMAGNETS

Pulsing magnetic forces are sometimes more effective than permanent magnets. Studies on research of magnetic fields for healing published in major scientific journals are usually based on the use of pulsating magnetic fields. Such instruments are widely used in Europe. Pulsing magnetic forces are usually more expensive, so one ought to try permanent magnets for most conditions first. In the next chapter some specific techniques for treating specific ailments or conditions with permanent magnets will be described.

NEXT TIME GET A MAGNETIZED HELMET

---

[*] An instrument called The Electronic Muscle Tester has been designed to make muscle testing more objective. It is manufactured by PsychoPhysics Labs (see references).

SPECIFIC TREATMENTS & PERSONAL REPORTS

Every person is unique and what works for one person may not work for another. Diet, vitality, mental attitude, social connections, and planetary positions* all contribute to one's general health. The following pages cover a few specific conditions and possible treatment procedures. These should be taken as possible starting points, not rigid prescriptions. The human body consists of many delicate interacting systems. For example, a woman came to me with injuries from a fall on a wet supermarket floor. She fell on her tail bone and was unable to sit on a flat surface. Naturally I treated her tail bone area, but there was no relief after several sessions. My intuition led me to treat the top of her head. The effect was excellent and after one sessions she said she could sit on a hard surface and after three sessions she was completely recovered. So please consider all possible factors when using magnets and continue to use or expand the use of herbs, traditional medicines, chiropractic adjustments, acupuncture, hypnosis, massage, and mental and emotional support.

---

* see chapter 10 for information on magnetism and planetary positions and magnetism and love.

SPECIFIC TREATMENTS - A FEW EXAMPLES

Asthma

Treat directly over the lungs with north pole to calm and relax breathing spasms and decrease inflammation. Treat the adrenal glands and kidneys (on the back just over the waist on each side of the spinal cord) with the south pole to stimulate the production of cortisone and keep water flowing through the system. Help the person express anger physically and verbally to allay future asthma attacks(to a dummy - a pillow or cushion, not necessarily a real person). Encourage swimming and other physical activities, the more strenuous, the better, once the asthma improves. Physical activity and emotional expression help stimulate the adrenal glands to produce more of a class of hormones called 'glucocorticoids', which reduce inflammation. These hormones are sometimes given in the form of inhaled sprays or injections to help reduce severe asthma attacks.

I had asthma for years; now I haven't a trace of it. The last time I had an attack was when I stayed at a friends house with eight cats who were house bound because of the winter temperature. Twenty minutes of north pole on my chest and I could breathe again. I slept on the couch, felt a bit wheezy when I woke up and another twenty minute treatment eliminated that - haven't had a wheeze for 15 years.

Arthritis

Treat the stiff areas, first with north if they are painful, then south to promote faster healing. Treat the adrenal test points located just below the shoulder blades with whatever feels best (probably south). I suggest taking cod liver oil, or equivalent oils. There are over 200 types of arthritis; not all types respond to magnetic therapy.

Insomnia

A magnetic bed can be helpful. Most magnetic beds have the north pole towards the body which can promote sleep. Or place a large permanent magnet on the chest for ten minutes (bionorth towards the body) before attempting sleep. Hypnosis training can be helpful as well. Hypnosis tapes played as one drifts off to sleep are wonderful. I use them every few nights.

Chronic Back Pain

Some back pains are related to kidney malfunctioning, liver problems, knee misalignments, or being overweight, which stress the back muscles. A chiropractor's treatments might be helpful in addition to magnetic treatments directly on the back. A number of companies make magnetic back pads, but often suggest using the north pole on the back. I've found the south pole is usually more effective.

Jet Lag

Kris Ihli, a professional healer from Mt. Shasta, California, reported successful treatment of jet lag by placing acupuncture magnets (of the appropriate polarity - determined by muscle testing) on the points known as the four gates. These are located between the thumbs and forefingers and between the big toes and first toes.

A Few Cases

Susan came to visit. She said she was feeling anxious and automatically picked up a large magnet that was lying around and placed it on her chest, with the bionorth side toward the chest. In one minute she said: "This is amazing! I feel much calmer already." In three or four minutes she said she felt fine and put the magnet down.

Another woman had a broken foot. After using magnetic treatments (biosouth) for a few days she called to say how much better her foot was. She said: "This is like the hand of an angel on my foot."

Rosemary wore a bracelet. It didn't help her; but then, nothing was wrong with her. She gave it to a friend who could not move her thumb without pain because of arthritis. After wearing the bracelet for a couple of weeks she could move her thumb freely without any pain.

Diane broke her foot and x-rays showed a gap that was not healing. After applying magnetic treatments for a only a week, x-rays showed the gap was filling in rapidly.

A woman with muscular dystrophy had progressed to the point of being in a wheelchair, unable to move her arms or legs. After three days of treatment by Richard Hopkins, a magnetic therapist in San Diego, she began to recover circulation in her legs. In four days her muscles, which had completely atrophied, began to physically grow. At the end of three weeks she could move her arms a little bit. At the time of this writing she continues to make progress.

Richard Hopkins reported to me that a woman who had been paralyzed for 38 years from a misapplied spinal block, reported her first bladder control (after three weeks of wearing four small ring magnets in a headband). She also experienced pain down the legs which is typical of nerve regeneration.

He also described the case story of a 68 year old woman who has been homebound with degeneration of the nerves in the legs making it hard to walk for more than ten years. She used a magnetic bed pad (with ring magnets 3 1/2 inch diameter inside it) for six months. She now can walk and no longer has pain.

Bob was awakened twice nightly for bathroom calls. After he used a magnet for about five days on his bladder area he found that he hardly ever needed to get up at night.

John, an elderly man, purchased a magnetic sleeping pad and reported that he quickly fell asleep now, whereas before he used to wake up in the middle of the night. He said his knees are not as stiff on humid or cold days as they used to be.

I met Betsy at a conference. She told me she broke her finger on the way to the conference and didn't want to stop for medical treatment. A friend gave her a magnet to tape on the finger. The next day she went to a doctor who x-rayed the finger and was amazed to find that it had already healed. The swelling had gone down and healing taken place in about 24 hours. This emphasizes the importance of immediate treatment. As soon as there is a break or injury, the body starts repairing itself.

Carl had a strange rash on his hands that had been present for some weeks. He began placing his hand on a large magnetic disc for a few minutes a day. The rash began to disappear within a week.

Gary wrote me saying he had purchased my earlier book and then broke his wrist. Not being willing to put it in a cast and lose time playing sports, he acquired a couple of domino magnets and placed them on his wrist, biosouth toward the body. His wrist healed very quickly and he was delighted because he didn't have any downtime.

Mary's wrist was hurting. She simply placed her wrist on a magnet from time to time when she thought of it, and the pain went away.

A 37 year old man injured his hip 20 years ago. After all that time it still became painful when he was especially active. Twenty minutes of magnetic treatment eliminated the pain. Nothing else had ever worked.

Japanese baseball player Hideki Irabu tapes tiny magnets to various pressure points on his throwing arm; they supposedly improve his circulation in the same way that acupuncture does, according to a Time Magazine story of July, '97.

Case studies could fill pages. But nothing will convince you as much as your own personal experience. If you have a painful condition, don't wait until you've read all the books and articles available. Try magnetic therapy immediately.

You can verify my observations on your house plants or your own body. If magnet treatments work half as well for you as they have for me and my friends; you will be delighted. I became such a believer that this is my third book on the subject. My curiosity has become a vocation.

- *Not all ailments or conditions respond to magnetic therapy.*

- *Consult a medical doctor, chiropractor, or acupuncturist for any serious condition.*

- *Magnets don't cure anything – they help the body's natural healing abilities.*

- *Magnetic treatments are compatible with all other treatments or medicines.*

Like most medical treatments, best results are obtained if treatment begins early. The earlier the better, and in fact the optimum time to treat is before you have any problem! Therefore, the next chapter deals with prevention.

PREVENTION

Stress, aging, and constitutional weakness can be helped. Magnetic treatments are ideal for sub-clinical minor chronic conditions. They are inexpensive, easy to apply, and have no side effects. They can be used in the home, office, or car without interfering with quiet activities. Sleeping in a magnetic bed requires no attention at all. It's generally a good thing to do once a week or so. I generally use the biosouth polarity, as I like to always feel energetic. People who have difficulty sleeping may prefer the bionorth polarity. As mentioned before, whole body treatment is not desirable if there are specific glands, organs, or body parts that require individual treatments of opposite magnetic force directions. Again, I say experiment. Do not take anyone's word as the gospel truth. Magnetism and health is still an infant science with many unknowns.

Placing each foot on a large magnet can be helpful for people at times. It's probably a good general preventative treatment. I usually find (by muscle testing) that biosouth on the right, bionorth on the left is the pattern my body likes as a general tonifier, but you may be different. Experiment. Notice any sensations. How aware can you be of what your body needs?

Wearing a magnetic necklace for a week every now and then can help keep your neck flexible. I found a magnetic bracelet also is strengthening, especially if I feel out of balance, or that I might be getting the sniffles.

Men over fifty might occasionally sit on a magnet (bionorth toward the body) to keep the prostrate gland in good health.

Two parts of the body that can be easily treated with beneficial results are the heart area and the thymus. Treating the heart area will increase blood flow according to independent studies done by two doctors, one in Germany and the other in the United States. Although these studies were done with pulsing magnetic fields, permanent magnets will presumably have similar, though less powerful, effects. A permanent magnet of a few hundred to a thousand gauss strength (biosouth towards the body) covering an area of at least 10 square inches would be good. Small neodymiums (one-inch diameter) are probably not as effective because the magnetic force direction turns horizontal an inch or so off center from the magnet surface. Use of the bionorth may make a person drowsy and can be useful for insomnia. I sometimes place bionorth on my chest when I want to take a nap, for example on a midday airplane trip.

Stronger is not necessarily better.
Strong magnets should not be used if
one has a pacemaker or heart problem.

The thymus gland, located just below the collarbone, plays a key role in the immune system. An occasional treatment with the biosouth polarity could give a little boost to the thymus, though I know of no research on this topic. A small magnet could be used, perhaps from 1/2 to 2 inches in diameter. Two cookie magnets placed on the inside and outside of a shirt would be ideal. The strength could be anything from one hundred gauss to two thousand gauss and the polarity should be biosouth, unless one has allergies or auto immune disease. In those cases it would probably be better to use bionorth to calm down the immune system.

MAGNETIC WATER

Drinking magnetically treated water seems like a good preventative technique. A German scientist, Dr. Peter Kokoschinegg, found that plants watered with biosouth treated water grew faster and larger than plants treated with tap water. He found that the plants treated with bionorth water grew less than controls. Dr. Mary Broeringmeyer, a pioneer in magnetic therapy, personally reported to me that plants watered with biosouth water grew faster. She also said that bionorth water placed in vases preserved flowers better than biosouth. I found that wheat sprouts watered with biosouth water grew faster than untreated controls and tasted sweeter than sprouts watered with bionorth water. There are several formal studies on plant growth and magnetized water, on treating seeds with magnetic fields, and treating the plants with permanent magnets as they grow from sprouts or seeds. These studies span many years and many countries (see references). Several companies sell magnets for treating water for enhancing crop growth. The magnets typically used are the standard domino type encased in various types of plastic holders.

Since magnetized water is good for plants it seems reasonable that it would be good for people too. Dick Wicks from Australia wrote me testifying to the value of drinking magnetized water to assist in healing a troublesome ailment he'd had for years. He was so impressed that he started a magnetic company in Australia and Penguin Press has recently assigned a

writer to prepare a book about his work that should be out early in 1998. Other personal reports about the value of drinking magnetized water are described in the book: Discovery of Magnetic Health. I have not seen any formal research studies on this, however. I started drinking magnetized water and have only been ill with a cold for one day in the two years since, except during a trip to Peru when I drank non-magnetized Peruvian water. Simply setting a jug of water on a magnetic disc of the desired polarity is the simplest and easiest way to obtain magnetic water. Some people who drink magnetic water prefer it to be treated with south polarity, while others prefer north polarity. Children seem to prefer north treated water and adults generally prefer south treated water.

I made an informal survey on over 100 people at a conference. The majority found the biosouth treated water tasted better than bionorth and both tasted much better than untreated city water. Dr. Bansal, a biomagnetic researcher in India, recommends washing the eyes and skin with magnetic water, and Dr. Mary Broeringmeyer reported it helped bed sores. Although some writers claim that water should only be treated with the north pole, I urge the reader to make their own tests before deciding which polarity to use as I have not seen any controlled studies on this topic.

In addition to water, you can treat beer, wine, juice, milk, or any liquid. I haven't tried treating ice cream yet. Perhaps some reader will do this experiment and let me know the results. Also unknown is whether or not that magnetically treated beer, wine, or ice cream will prevent ill effects from over consumption of these substances. Any volunteers for research?

Could it be that magnetic treatments help prevent illness? Probably. It helped mice avoid frostbite in one cruel study that subjected two groups of mice to freezing temperatures. The one that was pretreated with magnetism (polarity unstated) didn't get frostbitten. I had frostbite on a finger from a mountain climb as a youth. Twenty years later it began to turn white when I went swimming or got cold. I treated it with magnetism only three times and the symptoms vanished.

CANCER

In one study mice were pretreated with magnetism (and radio waves) before being inoculated with cancer cells. They didn't get cancer. Albert Davis and Walter Rawls, early researchers on biomagnetism reported similar preventative effects on mice with pretreatment with permanent magnets. Many studies and reports have shown that magnetic treatments help cancer, so it seems plausible that pretreatments for humans would be helpful. This would seem to be one argument for sleeping on a magnetic bed now and then.

Women concerned about breast cancer might try inserting small magnets in their bras. I came across a newspaper article about a study done at a clinic in Beijing, China where women were asked to wear magnetic bras. After ten years there were no cases of breast cancer. Although I don't have all the details, on general principles this is what I would expect. ONLY THE BIONORTH POLE SHOULD BE USED. If any women want to try this the tiny discs used by acupuncturists might be good to use[*].

Magnetic treatments seem to strengthen the body. One weight trainer uses magnets on muscles as they are exercised. Others use magnets after exercise if muscles are strained and painful because magnetic treatments increase blood flow. I place magnets on my chest prior to skiing, climbing to high altitude or running as it increase blood oxygen. Old injuries and genetically weak body parts should definitely be treated. The general suggestions for treatment are:

**IF IT HURTS NOW, TREAT IT WITH BIONORTH AND
IF THAT DOESN'T HELP, TREAT IT WITH BIOSOUTH.
IF WAS HURT IN THE PAST, TREAT IT WITH THE
    BIOSOUTH POLARITY.
IF YOU WANT TO STRENGTHEN IT NOW AND KEEP IT
    STRONG, TREAT IT WITH THE BIOSOUTH POLARITY.**

---

[*] Magnetic Bra inserts are available from PsychoPhysics Labs.

Since this is contrary to what some other biomagnetic therapists have claimed, the reader is urged to make his own tests as I have done and come to his or her own conclusions.

MAGNETISM & YOUTHING

The application of magnetic fields can prolong the life span of laboratory animals. Therefore, it's likely that magnetic treatments will also help humans live longer lives. Although major studies on human life span are difficult to do, it has been amply researched and demonstrated that magnetic treatments will definitely benefit human health. There is no question that magnetism is beneficial and helps promote health, flexibility, hormone production, and general energy. Anyone who applies magnets to the body following the principles outlined in this booklet will quickly verify that for themselves.

The evidence for longer life span is dramatically positive for animals. There are five reports on extended life span of mice by 33 to 100%. Two Chinese acupuncturists, Minda Hsu and Chikuo Fong, reported an experiment on extending the life of tadpoles. Five each were placed in glass beakers, filled with water. One beaker was treated with a magnetic field of 800 gauss (polarity unspecified), another was untreated. No food was given to the tadpoles. The ones in the magnetically treated beaker lived an average of 27 days, versus 21 days for the non-treated tadpoles. They also reported that mice placed in a cage shielded from natural earth magnetism died sooner than a control group.

What About Humans?

Although major studies have yet to be done on rejuvenation with humans, it seems like time to start.

Possible Procedures

Magnetic fields can be applied to the whole body in two ways:

1. Flat Magnetic Beds - either with permanent or pulsed magnetic fields.
2. Large magnetic coils which wrap around the whole body like giant tubes.

Before any whole body treatment procedure is undertaken, a person should have each gland and organ magnetically checked and treated with the appropriate polarity otherwise some glands or organs could be receiving the wrong polarity. The technique for doing this procedure is fully described in my other books (see references).

The Next Step

Plans are underway to set up a research laboratory to test specific frequencies, directions, and intensities of magnetic fields in order to find those which are most likely to produce longer life span. The results will most certainly be beneficial, but it may take a while to find out if life span will be expanded or health will simply be improved.

Resetting The Biological Clocks

If there are biological clocks they may be amenable to extension by the application of magnetic forces, which are known to be involved in DNA chain building. This may take some clever and/or elaborate instrumentation. And it might be done with simple instrumentation already available. It will probably require many helping hands and minds.

People who wish to participate may begin by subscribing to a quarterly newsletter (see chapter 10) and treating themselves according to guidelines published in the newsletter with the instruments and special coils now available, and modifications or new instruments as they are developed. They will be asked to report their observations to be published in the Newsletter and/or on the internet.

By this rapid means, everyone will help one another to quickly evolve the most efficacious treatment procedures, this will bypass years of laboratory research requiring thousands of dollars in funding, etc. There are hundreds of possible wave forms, pulse rates, and amplitudes to test. No one can try them all, but everyone working together can. It may take thousands of individual researchers to find what works in the most efficient manner. For frequencies under 30 and forces less than a few gauss no harmful results are likely; it is only a question of what or which pattern is most beneficial. Anyone who would like to participate in this exciting research should contact me at the address in the back of the book for more information.

My website is www.Buryl.com.

My E-Mail address is burylpayne@aol.com

SOURCES & REFERENCES

MAGNETS AND MAGNETIC DEVICES

Magnets may be purchased locally from industrial supply houses. The yellow pages in the phone book will give you that information. Magnets marked, coated, or encased in various garments from shoe inserts to magnetic beds are now manufactured by about twenty different companies. Other companies import garments from overseas, usually Taiwan, Korea, or Japan. Shop around; prices vary a lot for similar devices or magnets. Some companies are multilevel operations and you can take advantage of an opportunity to both use magnets and help others learn about them, while receiving compensation for your networking.

If you plan to purchase a magnetic garment, or bed, it would be a good idea to choose one which can be applied with either the north or south polarity so you can test and experiment (and you should check to determine if the polarity is as marked). Sometimes errors are made by manufacturers – or magnets may not be marked at all. Many garments are made with small magnets alternating in polarity. This may be satisfactory for many ailments that do not involve the whole body.

I have met or spoken by phone with most of the people manufacturing or selling magnets or garments. Without exception I have found them to be dedicated, sincere, honest people. Often they came to do this because they had some condition or ailment that was helped by magnetism. All of them have a strong desire to see this wonderful healing modality be widely available so that everyone will benefit.

If you want more information about magnetic therapy, the list of book and articles below will get you started.

BOOKS

Energy Therapy – Broeringmeyer, R. and M. Biohealth Enterprises, Inc. $45
P. 0. Box 628, Murray Hill, KY. 42071
1-800-626-3386.

Magnetic Therapy – Walls, Robert Allen.
P.O. Box 10382, McLean, VA 22101-1502, 1995

Biomagnetic & Herbal Therapy – Michael Tierra, Lotus Light Publications, 1997
P.O. Box 1008, Silver Lake, WI 53170
1-800-548-3824

Discovery of Magnetic Health – George J. Washnis and Richard Z. Hricak,
NOVA Publishing Company, 1993
11607 Nebel St.
Rockville, MD 20852
1-800-637-0067

Magnet Therapy – Holger Hannemann,
Sterling Publishing Company, Inc., 1990

The Body Magnetic – Buryl Payne, Ph. D.
PsychoPhysics Press, 1996, 1803 Mission, Suite 24, Santa Cruz, CA 95064

Advanced Magnetic Therapy – Buryl Payne, Ph.D.
Lotus Light Publications, 1999.
Available from PsychoPhysics Press.

How and Why We Age – Leonard Hayflick, Ph.D.
Ballentine Press, 1996.

NEWSLETTERS

Bio-Electro-Magnetics Institute Newsletter
John Zimmerman, editor.
2490 W. Moana Lane, Reno, NV 89509
Send Dr. Zimmerman $5 each for a list of manufacturers and suppliers of magnetic devices, or a list of magnetic beds, or a list of magnetic therapists. Send $10 for a subscription to his excellent newsletter.

Bioenergy Health Newsletter
475 State Rt. 94E, Murray, KY 42071.
Monthly newsletter about biomagnetics, nutrition, etc. from pioneer magnetic therapist, Dr. Mary Broering-meyer.

Magnetism and Youthing Newsletter
Dewey Lipe, Ph.D. editor.
Email:DeweyL@ix.netcom.com
5336 Harwood Rd. San Jose, CA 95124
A Quarterly newsletter of articles and reports on magnetic fields and other ways to extend lifespan. $25/yr.

ARTICLES

Only a few are listed that might be of interest to a reader; there are now probably 100 references available. Each article will usually give more references. Most articles are about pulsing magnetic fields.

Research Report/Magnetic Field Therapy
GMF Corporation A. G.
Alpen Str. 4
CH-6301 Zug. Switzerland
FAX 042-231618

"Geomagnetic Parameters and Psychiatric Hospital Admissions."
Friedman, H., and R.O. Becker. 1963.
Nature 200:626-628.

"Daily Repetitive Transcranial Magnetic Stimulation Improves Mood In Depression."
George, M.S., Wassermann, E.M., Williams, W.A., et. al. Neuroreport, 1995, 6, 1853-1856

"The Biomagnetic Effect: It's Application in Acupuncture Therapy." Hsu, M. and Fong, C.
Volume 6, issue 4 of The American Journal of Acupuncture. 1978.

"Exposure of Irrigation & Drinking Water to a Magnetic Field with Controlled Power & Direction."
Lin, I.J. and J. Yotvat (Department of Mineral Engineering, Technion, Haifa 32000, Israel).
Journal of Magnetism and Magnetic Materials, Vol. 83 pp. 525-526. 1990.

"Magnetic Treatments and Arthritis"
Markoll, Richard, et all.– Journal of Rheumatology, 1996.

"Correlation Between Heart Attack & Magnetic Activity." Molin, Srivostova S.R.C.
Nature, Vol. 277, Feb. 22, 1979.

Pittman, U.J. has ***four articles on magnetic treatment to increase plant growth*** in Volumes 44, 47, 50 and 57 of the Canadian Journal of Plant Science.

"Galvomagnetic Fluctuations & Disturbed Behavior." Pokorny and Mefferd.
Journal of Nervous and Mental Diseases, Vol. 143, No. 2, 1966.

"Reversal Of Vasoconstrictive Deficits In Parkinson's Disease By Application Of External Magnetic Fields: A Report Of Five Cases."
Sandyk, R. – International Journal of Neuroscience, 75, 213-228. (b) 1994

"Magnetised Water and Magnetised Oils,"
Santwani, M.T. Excerpt from: Magneto-Therapy For Common Diseasesfrom Bioenergy Health Newsletter, summer, 1997.

"Magnetic Sensitivity of the Pineal Gland."
Semm, P. Nature no. 228:206. 1980.

"Pineal Function in Mammals and Birds is Altered by Earth-Strength Magnetic Fields."
Semm, P. 1992. In M.C. Moore-Ede, S.S. Campbell & R.J. Reiter (editors). Electromagnetic Fields and Circadian Rhythms, 53-42, Birkhauser, Boston, 1992.

The Effect Of Oral Irrigation With A Magnetic Water Treatment Device On Plaque And Calculus
Watt, DL, et al – Journal of Clinical Peridontolgy, vol. 20, pp 314-317. 1993.

ORGANIZATIONS

International Magnetic Therapists Association
Centered in Australia - this organization has 8,000 members. Three levels of membership are available. If you are using magnets in any manner I urge you to join this organization so that we can take a united position and work with the government regulatory bodies everywhere to support the use of magnetic therapy. A United States branch will be established with conferences and newsletters as the use of magnetic therapy expands. Their address is: 103 North Main Rd, Nailsworth SA 5083, Australia Fax (618) 8344 5965, Phone 8344 6609, email ACONT@Bigpont.com

North American Academy of Magnetic Therapy
This group has a yearly convention and also a great newletter with recent studies and information.
28240 W. Agoura Rd., #202, Agoura, CA 91301
Nationwide phone (800) 457-1853

COMPUTER WEB SITES

The author publishes monthly bulletins on magnetic therapy for specific conditions, magnetic products, and other items of global health.   www.buryl.com

PSYCHOPHYSICS PRODUCTS- Books

THE BODY MAGNETIC

For me, the study of magnetism began with the discovery of a new force, one that is related to magnetism, but different from it. This force was initially found to be present as a spin force around the human body, and seems to be present around all matter from electrons to galaxies. It is quite large and easily detected by simple household materials.

Chapter III of *The Body Magnetic* describes how to make a detector and how this force relates to magnetism.

Another chapter in this book describes some of the fascinating and important properties of Earth's magnetic field and how this field is modulated by positions of the planets. These observations form the basis for helping transform astrology into a science.

One of the most practical chapters of this book gives the technique of using muscle testing to test the energy balance of each gland and organ in the body. This technique takes magnetic therapy to the next step towards becoming a science, especially when used in conjunction with the Electronic Muscle Tester described on the next page.   **$17.50 POSTPAID**

BIOMEDITATION

If you really want to learn hypnosis, *Biomeditation* is a great workbook with step by step instructions on induction techniques, unique processes for clearing the mind, techniques for preparing affirmations. A useful adjunct for the BioSensor.

$23.00 POSTPAID

LOVE & SEX WITHOUT CONFLICT

The mystery of love and sex is being uncovered. *Love And Sex Without Conflict* is a book which describes the connections between geomagnetic changes and love relationships. I've identified several types of love and their connection with different planets. Being merely descriptive is not enough for a practical guy like me, and I've included twenty simple techniques to help people get along better, even if the 'magnetism' is temporarily disruptive.

Love And Sex Without Conflict is available from PsychoPhysics Press for only $10 post paid, but it could be worth ten thousand dollars to you if it helps you save your marriage. **$10.00**

ARTICLES ON MAGNETISM By Buryl Payne.

- Arthritis and Magnetism
- Cancer and Magnetic Therapy
- Channeled Material on Magnetism
- Shoulder Pains and Magnetic Therapy
- The Power of Thought to Influence the Sun
- Chronic Fatigue Syndrome & Magnetic Therapy
- Measurement of the Aura--A Higher Octave of Magnetism
- Magnetic Diagnosis and Treatment of All Glands and Organs
- The Sounds of Earth's Magnetic field; Its Influence on Health

EACH ARTICLE IS $3 EA. OR 5 FOR $12, OR ALL FOR $20.

PSYCHOPHYSICS PRODUCTS- Tools & Misc.
THE BIOSENSOR

Every injury, ailment, disease, imbalance or stressed condition will usually be helped by enlisting the power of the mind. Hypnosis, or what I call 'applied meditation, has been around a long time. Its application can be augmented by use of an instrument which detects the sympathetic nervous system activity. A meter and speaker provide simultaneous indication of the activity level. Stress and emotion increase this activity; when it is lowered the mind/body is more receptive to healing directives. The practical techniques for using this instrument have been fully described in my book: *Biomeditation.*   **$150.00**

THE ELECTRONIC MUSCLE TESTER (accessory)

By addition of a magnetic transducer to the BioSensor, it can be used to measure finger strength. This can be used to determine which polarity of a magnet is strengthening for the body. Or it can be used to determine which food or supplement, herb, or homeopathic remedy, etc. would be good to take at the time of testing. Although still primitive compared with what is on the drawing boards, it is a useful tool for those interested in self testing to improving their health in an efficient and cost effective manner. **$50.00**

PSYCHOENERGETICS FITNESS DECK

A Novel Exercise Program - Like to exercise but find it boring? Want to do it at home, while traveling, while sunning at the beach? If so, the PsychoEnergetics Fitness Card Deck may be just the thing. A set of 52 exercises from kundalini yoga and other sources are illustrated on 4 x 6 cards. Shuffle and draw four for a daily exercise set which will be pleasantly different every time. There's even a joker in the deck which says go back to bed, don't exercise today! **$17. 50**

PULSED MAGNETIC GENERATORS
CUSTOM INSTRUMENTS FOR RESEARCH
Available from PsychoPhysics Labs. Call for prices.

THE DYNAMIC SOLAR SYSTEM -
A COMPUTER SOFTWARE PROGRAM

This program shows the solar system in motion. It can be set for any date from 10,000 years in the past to 10,000 years in the future. The planets will move faster or slower as you wish and display the numerical positions at the click of the mouse. A lengthy text on the disc explains the connections between planetary positions, solar activity, and geomagnetism. A fascinating and educational delight! **$60.00**

MAGNETISM & YOUTHING PROJECT

Please refer to the last page of chapter 9 of this book regarding this project.

Or write or email

Dewey Lipe, Ph. D.
Executive Director
5336 Harwood Rd.
San Jose, CA 95124
DewelyL@ix.netcom.com
burylpayne@aol.com
www.buryl.com

PSYCHOPHYSICS PRICE LIST*

1. The Body Magnetic Book — $17.50
2. Biomeditation Book — $23.00
3. Love & Sex Without Conflict Book — $10.00
4. Articles by B.Payne $3@, 5/$12, complete set $20.00
5. The Biosensor — $150.00
6. Electronic Muscle Tester (accessory) — $ 50.00
7. PsychoEnergetics Fitness Deck — $17.50
8. Pulsed Magnetic Generator & — call for price
   Custom Instruments
9. Dynamic Solar System – software — $60.00
10. Magnetism & Youthing Project — $50.00
11. Magnetism & Youthing Newsletter 1 yr.subs. $25.00

Prices include postage shipping and handling.

MAIL ORDER WITH YOUR CHECK MADE TO:
PSYCHOPHYSICS PRESS, 1803 Mission St. Suite 24,
Santa Cruz, CA 95060   USA   (831) 462-1588

ORDER FORM – **Please mail me the following:**

ITEM DESCRIPTION	QTY	UNIT PRICE	PRICE EXTENSION
PLEASE SEND ORDER TO BELOW:		TOTAL	$

NAME:

ADDRESS: